How to use this book

We all love kittens and this book is packed full of charming kitties! Make a wall chart of the cutest kittens around. Choose from among the 28 large kitten stickers to create a chart of your favorites.

Over 30 stickers of adorable kitties!

Pick your favorite 12 stickers and place them on the chart. If you change your mind, you can add another sticker!

Bonus kitten stickers to decorate whatever you like!

My Favorite Kittens

The pages inside tear out and become nine mini posters for you to keep!

Ginger tabby

Grey tabby shorthair

Black Scottish Fold

Brown tabby Maine Coon

Persian kittens

Burmese

British longhair

Siamese

Grey Scottish Folds

Ginger Siberian

Brown tabby shorthair

Tortoiseshell shorthair

Gray tabby shorthair

Burmese

Gray Scottish Folds

British longhair

Siamese

Brown tabby shorthair

Tortoiseshell shorthair

My Favorite Kittens

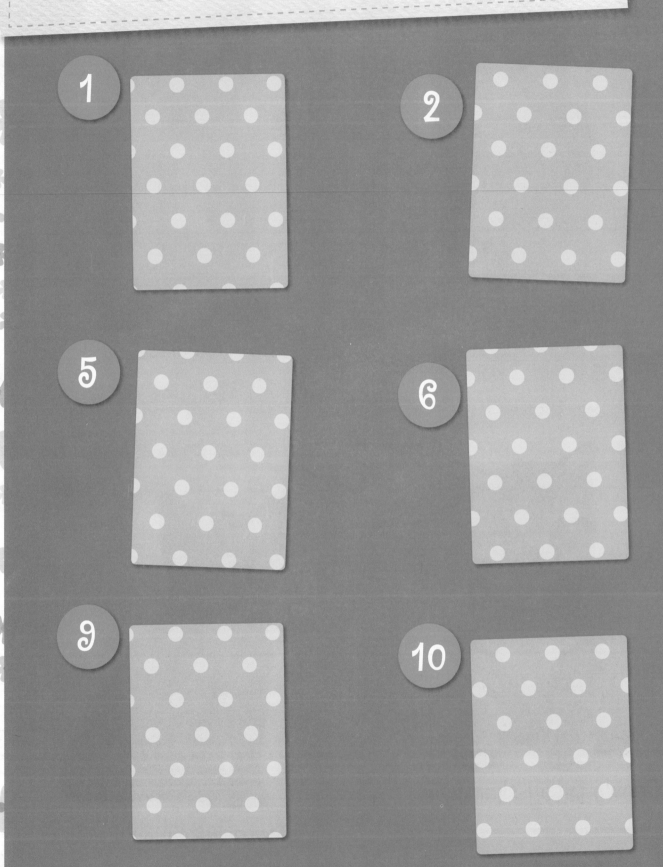

1

2

5

6

9

10

Gray tabby shorthair

Tricolored shorthair

Black-and-white shorthair

British shorthair

Brown tabby Scottish Fold

Black Persian

Blue tabby point birman

Black shorthair

Norwegian Forest

Birman

British longhair

Siamese

White Cornish Rex

Tabby-and-white shorthair

Bicolor British longhair

Tabby Serengeti

177527-03029-001-052818

Tortoiseshell Persian

Tortoiseshell shorthair

Brown Abyssinian

Ginger Maine Coon

British Blue

Ginger tabby shorthair

White exotic shorthair

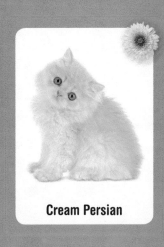

Cream Persian

Black-and-white Persian

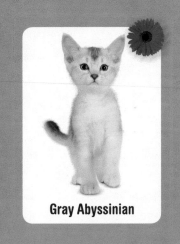

Gray Abyssinian

Here are some bonus stickers

Brown tabby Bengal

Burmese

Persian kittens

Ginger tabby

Ginger Siberian

Brown tabby Maine Coons

Black Scottish Fold